Charles M. Schulz

SNOOPY
and
THE PEANUTS GANG

ARE MAGIC

C000082606

RAVETTE BOOKS

This edition first published by Ravette Books Limited 1989.

Printed and bound for Ravette Books Limited,
3 Glenside Estate, Star Road,
Partridge Green, Horsham,
Sussex RH13 8RA
by Mateu Cromo Artes Gráfica, s.a.

ISBN: 1 85304 108 4

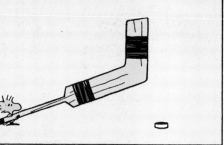

PEANUTS
featuring
"Good ol' Charlie Brown"
by Schulz

YES, MA'AM... I'M READY..

THIS IS "SHOW AND TELL" TIME...

FOR ALL YOU LUCKY KIDS OUT THERE IN CLASSROOM-LAND I'VE BROUGHT MY FAMOUS LEAF COLLECTION!

10-17

BUT FIRST, A WORD FROM MY SPONSOR..

THESE LEAVES ARE BROUGHT TO YOU THROUGH THE COURTESY OF OUR COUNTRY'S TREES

MY LEAF COLLECTION WAS GATHERED FROM MANY LAWNS AND ALONG-SIDE MANY CURBS... THESE ARE LEAVES FROM ALL WALKS OF LIFE...

AND NOW A BRIEF WORD FROM MY CO-SPONSOR, THE RAIN...

THE RAIN COMES DOWN FROM THE CLOUDS WHICH ARE IN THE SKY, AND WATERS THE SOIL UPON WHICH SIT THE TREES WHEREON GREW THESE LEAVES...

WHICH BRINGS US BACK TO MY FAMOUS COLLECTION.. YES, MA'AM?

FIRST THEY WANT YOU TO SHOW AND TELL, AND THEN THEY DON'T WANT YOU TO SHOW AND TELL...

SCHULZ

10-24

BOOT!

OOF!

PEANUTS
featuring
"Good ol' Charlie Brown"
by Schulz

HERE WE ARE, SNOOPY, SITTING IN A PUMPKIN PATCH WAITING FOR THE "GREAT PUMPKIN"

EVERY HALLOWEEN THE GREAT PUMPKIN FLIES THROUGH THE AIR WITH HIS BAG OF TOYS

AND JUST THINK..IF YOU AND I SIT HERE ALL NIGHT, WE MAY GET TO SEE HIM!

I REALLY APPRECIATE YOUR SITTING OUT HERE WITH ME, SNOOPY...

10-31

I MUST ADMIT, HOWEVER, THAT I'VE BEEN WONDERING WHY YOU'RE WEARING THOSE DARK GLASSES...

THERE ARE CERTAIN TIMES WHEN YOU PREFER NOT TO BE RECOGNIZED!

11-7

HEE
HEE
HEE
HEE

WHY DO SOME PEOPLE THINK IT'S FUNNY TO TALK ABOUT WORMS WHILE YOU'RE TRYING TO EAT SPAGHETTI?

PEANUTS
featuring
"Good ol' Charlie Brown"
by Schulz

PSYCHIATRIC HELP 5¢

THE DOCTOR IS IN

I WONDER IF IT'S POSSIBLE REALLY TO MAKE A FRESH START...

PSYCHIATRIC HELP 5¢

THE DOCTOR IS IN

SEE THAT PLANE UP THERE?

IT'S FILLED WITH PEOPLE WHO ARE ALL GOING SOMEPLACE..THAT'S WHAT I'D LIKE TO DO.. GO OFF SOMEPLACE, AND START A NEW LIFE...

FORGET IT, CHARLIE BROWN...WHEN YOU GOT OFF THE PLANE, YOU'D STILL BE THE SAME PERSON YOU ARE...

THE DOCTOR IS IN

11-14

BUT MAYBE WHEN I GOT TO THIS NEW PLACE, THE NEW PEOPLE WOULD LIKE ME BETTER

ONLY UNTIL THEY GOT TO KNOW YOU, CHARLIE BROWN..THEN YOU'D BE RIGHT BACK WHERE YOU STARTED..

BUT MAYBE THESE NEW PEOPLE WOULD BE MORE UNDERSTANDING

PEOPLE ARE PEOPLE, CHARLIE BROWN...

WELL, MAYBE I..

THE DOCTOR IS IN

FORGET IT, CHARLIE BROWN

BUT..

NOPE!

UH..

THE DOCTOR IS IN

THE DOCTOR IS IN

FIVE CENTS, PLEASE

SIGH

THE DOCTOR IS IN

ONCE YOU HAVE A PATIENT HOOKED, LAND HIM!

THE DOCTOR IS IN

PEANUTS
featuring
"Good ol'
CharlieBrown"
by SCHULZ

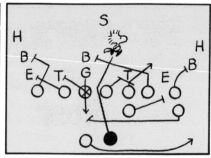

11-21

boot!

boot!
boot!
boot!

boomp!

boot!
boot!
boot!
boot!
boot!

boot! boot!
boot! boot!
((( )))

boot! boot!
boot! boot!
boot!
boot!
boot!

BANG!

THAT WAS AN EXCITING
FIRST QUARTER..

PEANUTS
featuring
"Good ol' Charlie Brown"
by SCHULZ

Y'WANNA HEAR SOMETHING FUNNY?

A WEIRD THING HAPPENED TO ME THE OTHER DAY, CHUCK..I HAD TO DELIVER A MESSAGE FOR MY DAD TO A FRIEND OF HIS WHO WORKS IN A BARBER SHOP, AND WHEN I WALKED IN, ONE OF THE BARBERS SAID TO ME, "WHAT CAN I DO FOR YOU, SON?"

THAT'S FUNNY!

SOMETHING LIKE THAT HAPPENED IN MY DAD'S BARBER SHOP ONCE A LONG TIME AGO... A MAN BROUGHT HIS GRANDDAUGHTER IN, AND THE BARBER THOUGHT THE LITTLE GIRL WAS A BOY, AND CUT OFF ALL HER CURLS! THE MOTHER WAS REALLY MAD...

EVERYONE WAS YELLING AND SCREAMING..BUT THOSE THINGS HAPPEN, I GUESS..AFTER IT'S ALL OVER, IT'S REALLY KIND OF FUNNY...

I WASN'T FINISHED WITH MY STORY, CHUCK!

11-28

SCHULZ

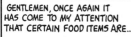

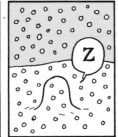

PEANUTS.
featuring
"Good ol' Charlie Brown"
by SCHULZ

CHOMP CHOMP CHOMP

RATS.. I'M STILL HUNGRY..

MAYBE I CAN GET AN ADVANCE ON TOMORROW NIGHT'S DINNER..

ANOTHER ADVANCE?

I DON'T KNOW WHAT I'M GOING TO DO WITH YOU..

1-2

$365 \times 5 = 1825$

ALL RIGHT, HERE YOU ARE, BUT I WANT YOU TO KNOW I JUST FIGURED OUT SOMETHING...

YOU ARE NOW FIVE YEARS AHEAD OF YOURSELF ON DINNERS!

SO WHAT'S WRONG WITH A LITTLE DEFICIT EATING?

PEANUTS
featuring
"Good ol' Charlie Brown"
by Schulz

HERE SHE COMES..

OKAY, CHUCK, I'M ALL SET FOR THE HOCKEY GAME...HOW DO WE PLAY?

WELL, YOU AND I WILL BE CENTERS... WE'LL FACE-OFF HERE IN THE MIDDLE..

I'm Reg. U.S. Pat. Off.—all rights reserved
© 1972 by United Feature Syndicate, Inc.

LINUS AND SCHROEDER WILL BE WINGS..

THE IDEA IS TO SHOOT THE PUCK BETWEEN THOSE CHUNKS OF SNOW...THE GOALIE, OF COURSE, WILL TRY TO STOP YOU...

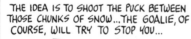

WHICH ONE IS THE GOALIE?

THE GOALIE IS THE ONE WEARING THOSE PADS...

1-23

PEANUTS
featuring
"Good ol' Charlie Brown"
by SCHULZ

DOG FOR SALE

DO YOU THINK PETS ARE IMPORTANT?

SURE

A FRIEND OF MINE AT SCHOOL GOT SOME GOLDFISH FOR HIS BIRTHDAY, BUT I DON'T THINK HE REALLY WANTED THEM..

PEOPLE BUY PETS FOR STRANGE REASONS

HOW DID YOU HAPPEN TO GET SNOOPY, CHARLIE BROWN?

WELL, I'M NOT QUITE SURE BECAUSE I WAS KIND OF YOUNG..

1-30

I THINK IT STARTED BECAUSE OF SOMETHING THAT HAPPENED AT A PLAYGROUND... I WAS PLAYING IN A SANDBOX WITH A COUPLE OF OTHER KIDS...I CAN'T EVEN REMEMBER WHO THEY WERE...

ANYWAY, ALL OF A SUDDEN, ONE OF THEM POURED A WHOLE BUCKET OF SAND OVER MY HEAD... I STARTED CRYING, I GUESS, AND MY MOTHER CAME RUNNING UP, AND TOOK ME HOME

IT'S KIND OF EMBARRASSING NOW TO TALK ABOUT IT

ANYWAY, THE NEXT DAY WE DROVE OUT TO THE DAISY HILL PUPPY FARM AND MY MOTHER AND DAD BOUGHT ME A DOG...

GOOD GRIEF!

SCHULZ

PEANUTS
featuring
"Good ol'
Charlie Brown"
by Schulz

HERE, I BOUGHT YOU SOMETHING..

HOW NICE!

I SAW YOU GIVE SOMETHING TO SNOOPY... WHAT WAS IT?

I GAVE HIM A FLEA COLLAR

2-6

THE ONLY TROUBLE WAS, IT TOOK ME AN HOUR TO GET IT ON THE FLEA!

PEANUTS featuring "Good ol' Charlie Brown" by SCHULZ

2-13

SOME FRIENDSHIPS ARE DOOMED FROM THE VERY BEGINNING!

DO YOU THINK IT'S POSSIBLE FOR SOMEONE TO BE IN LOVE AND NOT KNOW IT?

YOU MEAN ME, DON'T YOU?

YOU'RE TALKING ABOUT ME, AREN'T YOU? WHY DON'T YOU COME RIGHT OUT AND SAY IT? WHY DON'T YOU ADMIT IT?

2-20

WHY DON'T YOU JUST ASK ME IF I THINK IT'S POSSIBLE THAT I'M IN LOVE WITH YOU, AND I DON'T KNOW IT?

SCHROEDER, DO YOU THINK IT'S POSSIBLE THAT YOU'RE IN LOVE WITH ME, AND YOU DON'T KNOW IT?

NO!

LOVE DRIVES ME CRAZY!

PEANUTS
featuring
"Good ol' Charlie Brown"
by Schulz

OH, COME ON NOW.. BE REASONABLE!

I TRY TO DO MY BEST! I ALWAYS HAVE YOUR SUPPER READY ON TIME, AND I ALWAYS TRY TO FIX IT JUST THE WAY YOU WANT IT..

BUT NOW YOU'RE GOING TOO FAR!

OH, ALL RIGHT.. I'LL SEE WHAT I CAN DO... I MUST BE OUT OF MY MIND...

SOMETIMES EVEN I CAN'T BELIEVE HOW WISHY-WASHY I AM..

2-27

YOU WILL? GOOD... I REALLY APPRECIATE IT..

SO WHAT'S WRONG WITH WANTING TO BE SERVED BY A BEAUTIFUL WAITRESS?

Schulz

PEANUTS featuring "Good ol' Charlie Brown" by Schulz

HEY, MANAGER, I'VE GOT A GREAT IDEA!

WHY DON'T WE SELL OUR TEAM, AND MOVE TO A DIFFERENT CITY? THAT'S WHAT EVERYONE ELSE IS DOING

WE COULD SELL OUR TEAM, AND GET A FRESH START IN A NEW CITY

I'VE GOT A BETTER IDEA...WHY DON'T WE KEEP OUR TEAM, AND JUST SELL YOU?!

3-19

THE NEXT TIME I GET A GREAT IDEA, I'LL KEEP IT TO MYSELF!

PEANUTS

featuring "Good ol' Charlie Brown"

by Schulz

IS IT? IT **IS**!!

THE EASTER BEAGLE IS COMING!!

THANK YOU.. THANK YOU VERY MUCH

THANK YOU

THANK YOU

THANK YOU

4-2

THANK YOU VERY MUCH

SORRY, KID... THAT'S THE WAY IT GOES!

PEANUTS
featuring
"Good ol' Charlie Brown"
by SCHULZ

THIS IS RIDICULOUS

STUPID IS THE WORD!

IT'S NEVER GOING TO STOP RAINING! I'M GOING HOME!

BUT WHAT ABOUT THE GAME?

IT'LL PROBABLY CLEAR UP ANY MINUTE NOW... I THINK I SEE THE SUN..

WHERE'S EVERYONE GOING? DON'T GO! WE HAVE A GAME TO PLAY! COME BACK!!

YOU'RE OUT OF YOUR MIND, CHARLIE BROWN! ANYONE WHO WOULD STAND OUT IN THIS RAIN SHOULD SEE A PSYCHIATRIST!

MAYBE SHE'S RIGHT...

WELL, HELLO, THERE.. WHAT CAN I DO FOR YOU?

PSYCHIATRIC HELP 5¢

THE DOCTOR IS IN

I THINK THERE MUST BE SOMETHING WRONG WITH ME.. I DON'T SEEM TO KNOW ENOUGH TO GET IN OUT OF THE RAIN..

THAT'S VERY INTERESTING..

I JUST GET SO INVOLVED IN THESE BASEBALL GAMES I JUST SORT OF FORGET EVERYTHING ELSE, AND I JUST KIND OF LOSE TRACK OF EVERYTHING AND..

YOU KNOW WHAT?

WHAT?

THE DOCTOR IS IN

I'M GETTING WET!

THE DOCTOR

4-9

PEANUTS featuring "Good ol' Charlie Brown" by Schulz

I HAVE A QUESTION..

WHAT DO YOU THINK THE SECRET OF LIVING IS, CHUCK?

THE SECRET OF LIVING IS TO OWN A CONVERTIBLE AND A LAKE..

A CONVERTIBLE AND A LAKE?

4-16

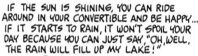

IF THE SUN IS SHINING, YOU CAN RIDE AROUND IN YOUR CONVERTIBLE AND BE HAPPY... IF IT STARTS TO RAIN, IT WON'T SPOIL YOUR DAY BECAUSE YOU CAN JUST SAY, "OH, WELL, THE RAIN WILL FILL UP MY LAKE!"

WHAT DO YOU THINK THE SECRET OF LIVING IS, SNOOPY?

SMAK!

Tm. Reg. U.S. Pat. Off.—All rights reserved
© 1972 by United Feature Syndicate, Inc.

A CONVERTIBLE AND A LAKE.. I DON'T KNOW ABOUT YOU, CHUCK...

IF YOUR LAKE IS DRYING UP, YOU CAN SAY, "OH, WELL, THIS IS NICE WEATHER FOR RIDING IN A CONVERTIBLE.."

PEANUTS
featuring
"Good ol'
Charlie Brown"
by Schulz

4-30

I HOPE I HELPED HIM, BUT I DON'T KNOW...

TEN MINUTES BEFORE YOU GO TO A PARTY IS NO TIME TO BE LEARNING HOW TO DANCE!

PEANUTS
featuring
"Good ol' Charlie Brown"
by SCHULZ

HEY, MANAGER!

OH, NO...NOW WHAT?

AS SOON AS I HEAR HER SAY, "HEY, MANAGER," MY STOMACH STARTS TO HURT...

AS SOON AS SHE SAYS, "HEY, MANAGER," I GET THIS BURNING IN MY STOMACH BECAUSE I KNOW SHE'S GOING TO COME UP WITH SOME STUPID SUGGESTION, OR SOME SARCASTIC REMARK OR SOME SORT OF DUMB...

5-7

HEY, MANAGER, I JUST WANT TO WISH YOU LUCK IN TODAY'S GAME...

HOW'S YOUR STOMACH?!

SCHULZ

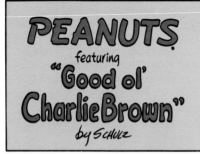

PEANUTS
featuring
"Good ol' Charlie Brown"
by SCHULZ

IS LOVE A 'NOW' KIND OF THING, CHUCK, OR IS IT MOSTLY HOPE AND MEMORIES?

WELL, MY DAD SAYS THAT HE TOOK A GIRL TO THE MOVIES ONCE, AND IT WAS ONE OF THOSE REAL SAD LOVE STORIES...

HE REMEMBERED THAT ANNE BAXTER WAS IN IT, AND FOR YEARS AFTERWARD, EVERY TIME HE SAW ANNE BAXTER, HE'D GET REAL DEPRESSED BECAUSE IT WOULD REMIND HIM OF THAT MOVIE AND THE GIRL HE HAD BEEN WITH...

5-21

HE NEVER FORGOT THAT GIRL BECAUSE EVERY TIME HE SAW ANNE BAXTER, IT WOULD REMIND HIM OF HER...

THEN, ONE NIGHT ON THE LATE, LATE SHOW, THAT SAME MOVIE CAME ON, BUT IT TURNED OUT THAT HE HAD BEEN WRONG ALL THOSE YEARS... IT WASN'T ANNE BAXTER... IT WAS SUSAN HAYWARD!

LOVE HAS ITS MEMORIES, I GUESS

I WAS REALLY HOPING IT WAS A 'NOW' KIND OF THING

IT IS FOR SOME OF US, SWEETIE!

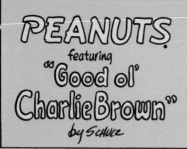

PEANUTS featuring "Good ol' Charlie Brown" by Schulz

6-4

PEANUTS featuring *"Good ol' CharlieBrown"* by Schulz

STRIKE TWO!

STRIKE THREE!

Tm. Reg. U. S. Pat. Off.—All rights reserved © 1972 by United Feature Syndicate, Inc.

RATS!

I'LL NEVER BE A BIG-LEAGUE PLAYER! I JUST DON'T HAVE IT! ALL MY LIFE I'VE DREAMED OF PLAYING IN THE BIG LEAGUES, BUT I KNOW I'LL NEVER MAKE IT...

YOU'RE THINKING TOO FAR AHEAD, CHARLIE BROWN...WHAT YOU NEED TO DO IS TO SET YOURSELF MORE IMMEDIATE GOALS...

7-2

IMMEDIATE GOALS?

YES

START WITH THIS NEXT INNING WHEN YOU GO OUT TO PITCH..

SEE IF YOU CAN WALK OUT TO THE MOUND WITHOUT FALLING DOWN!

PEANUTS
featuring "Good ol' Charlie Brown"
by Schulz

I SAW A MOVIE RECENTLY ABOUT A BOY AND HIS DOG

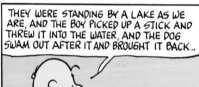

THEY WERE STANDING BY A LAKE AS WE ARE, AND THE BOY PICKED UP A STICK AND THREW IT INTO THE WATER, AND THE DOG SWAM OUT AFTER IT AND BROUGHT IT BACK..

7-9

I'M GOING TO HAVE TO STOP WATCHING THOSE MOVIES

PEANUTS featuring "Good ol' Charlie Brown" by SCHULZ

7-16

Tm. Reg. U.S. Pat. Off.—All rights reserved
© 1972 by United Feature Syndicate, Inc.

SCHULZ

PEANUTS
featuring
"Good ol' Charlie Brown"
by SCHULZ

PSYCHIATRIC HELP 5¢

THE DOCTOR IS | WAY OUT

PSYCHIATRIC HELP 5¢

I NEED SOME ADVICE

THE DOCTOR IS | IN

GOOD.. THAT'S WHAT I'M HERE FOR..

THE DOCTOR IS | IN

THERE'S THIS BOY I KIND OF LIKE, SEE, BUT HE NEVER PAYS ANY ATTENTION TO ME.. IS IT BECAUSE I'M UNATTRACTIVE?

THE DOCTOR IS | IN

7-23

HELP 5¢

NONSENSE! YOU'RE A VERY BEAUTIFUL YOUNG GIRL, AND YOU SHOULDN'T HAVE TO CHASE AFTER ANYONE!

THE DOCTOR

DO YOU REALLY THINK SO?

IE DOCTOR IS | IN

OF COURSE! WOULD I LIE TO YOU?

THE DOCTOR IS | IN

MY PSYCHIATRIST SAYS, "BLEAH!!"

PEANUTS
featuring
"Good ol' Charlie Brown"
by SCHULZ

THAT WAS A GOOD DIVE..

HAD IT BEEN INTO MY WATER DISH, I WOULD EVEN CALL IT A BEAUTIFUL DIVE...HOWEVER, IT WAS NOT INTO MY WATER DISH... IT WAS INTO MY SUPPER DISH!

8-13

PEANUTS
featuring
"Good ol' Charlie Brown"
by Schulz

I THINK IT WAS ONE OF THE BEST MOVIES I'VE EVER SEEN...

I KNEW YOU'D LIKE IT

SIP!

AFTERWARD, WE WENT TO THIS ART GALLERY, AND SAW ALL OF THESE WILD NEW PAINTINGS...

SOME OF THEM, OF COURSE, WERE QUITE HUGE...

THERE WAS ONE THAT WAS ALL DIFFERENT SHADES OF RED..

SIP!

8-20

I LIKE RED, OF COURSE, BUT I'M NOT SURE IF I LIKE IT THAT MUCH, AND..

SIP!

HI! DRINKING LEMONADE, I SEE! HOW ABOUT LETTING ME HAVE A SIP?

DON'T BE STUPID!!

SIP!

YOU THINK I WANT TO SIP FROM THE SAME STRAW YOU'VE BEEN SLURPING ON ?! GET OUT OF HERE!

ANYWAY, THERE WERE A LOT OF NICE PAINTINGS, AND..

SIP!

YOU KNOW, IT'S HARD TO TALK TO YOU WHEN YOU KEEP MAKING ALL THOSE STRANGE FACES!

THE YEARS ARE GOING BY...

I'M SCARED, CHUCK... WHAT IF I GROW UP, AND NO ONE EVER LOVES ME? WE PEOPLE WITH BIG NOSES ARE VERY INSECURE...

DO YOU THINK I HAVE A BIG NOSE, CHUCK? DO YOU THINK SOMEONE WILL LOVE ME SOMEDAY?

SURE

SURE?! "SURE," WHAT? "SURE" I HAVE A BIG NOSE, OR "SURE" SOMEONE WILL LOVE ME SOMEDAY?

MAYBE SOMEDAY THE REST OF YOUR FACE WILL CATCH UP WITH YOUR NOSE, AND THEN SOMEONE WILL LOVE YOU

9-17

HURRY UP, FACE!

PEANUTS featuring "Good ol' Charlie Brown" *by Schulz*

HERE'S ONE FROM IOWA...AND HERE'S ONE FROM PENNSYLVANIA..

Advice For Dog Owners

type type type

"DEAR SIR, I HAVE A DOG WHO CONTINUALLY SCRATCHES HIS EARS...WHAT SHOULD I DO? SIGNED, 'WONDERING'"

Dear Wondering, What I'm wondering is how you can be so dumb! Take your dog to the vet right away, stupid.

type type type type

"DEAR SIR, WE HAVE THREE PUPPIES WHO HAVE ENLARGED JOINTS AND ARE LAME... WHAT DO YOU THINK CAUSED THIS, AND WHAT SHOULD WE DO? SIGNED, 'DOG OWNER'"

9-24

Dear Dog Owner, Why don't you take up rock collecting? You're too stupid to be a dog owner. In the meantime, call your vet immediately.

type type type type

"DEAR SIR, MY DOG HAS BEEN COUGHING LATELY... WHAT SHOULD I DO? SIGNED, 'CONFUSED'"

Dear Confused, You're not confused, you're just not very smart. Now, you get that dog to the vet right away before I come over and punch you in the nose!

type type type

I WRITE A VERY FIRM COLUMN!

PEANUTS featuring "Good ol' Charlie Brown" by Schulz

WHAT A GREAT TITLE!

Toodle-oo, Caribou! A Tale of the Frozen North

One morning, Joe Eskimo went out to his barn to milk his polar cow. As he walked through the barn, tiny polar mice scampered across the frozen floor.

HMM..

I HATE TO TELL YOU THIS, BUT THERE ISN'T SUCH A THING AS A POLAR COW..

THERE ISN'T?

10-1

OKAY, SCRATCH THE POLAR COW..

THERE AREN'T SUCH THINGS AS POLAR MICE, EITHER...

THERE AREN'T?

OKAY, SCRATCH THE POLAR MICE... SIGH..

SOME OF MY BEST NOVELS NEVER GET OFF THE GROUND..

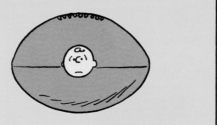

PEANUTS featuring "Good ol' Charlie Brown" by Schulz

♫ CHARLIE BROWNNNN ♫

I'LL HOLD THE FOOTBALL, CHARLIE BROWN, AND YOU COME RUNNING UP, AND KICK IT..

I CAN'T

I NEVER DO ANYTHING WITHOUT CONSULTING MY PSYCHIATRIST...

WELL, YOU GO TALK WITH YOUR PSYCHIATRIST, AND SEE WHAT YOU WANT TO DO...OKAY?

PSYCHIATRIC HELP 5¢

THE DOCTOR IS IN

I HAVE A STRANGE PROBLEM

THERE'S THIS GIRL, SEE, AND SHE'S ALWAYS TRYING TO GET ME TO KICK THIS FOOTBALL, BUT SHE ALSO ALWAYS PULLS IT AWAY AND I LAND ON MY BACK AND KILL MYSELF...

SHE SOUNDS LIKE AN INTERESTING GIRL...SORT OF A FUN TYPE...

I GET THE IMPRESSION THAT YOU HAVE A REAL NEED TO KICK THIS FOOTBALL...I THINK YOU SHOULD TRY IT!

I THINK YOU SHOULD TRY IT BECAUSE IN MEDICAL TERMS, YOU HAVE WHAT WE CALL THE "NEED TO NEED TO TRY IT"

I'M GLAD I TALKED WITH MY PSYCHIATRIST BECAUSE THIS YEAR I'M GONNA KICK THAT BALL CLEAR TO THE MOON!

AUGH!

WUMP

UNFORTUNATELY, CHARLIE BROWN, YOUR AVERAGE PSYCHIATRIST KNOWS VERY LITTLE ABOUT KICKING FOOTBALLS

10-8

PEANUTS
featuring
"Good ol'
Charlie Brown"
by SCHULZ

type
type
type
type

Toodle-oo, Caribou!
A Tale of the
Frozen North

The stall was empty!
"Someone has stolen my
polar cow!" shouted Joe Eskimo.

"This is the work
of Joe Jacket,
who hates me!"

MAY I SEE HOW
YOUR NEW NOVEL IS
COMING ALONG?

BE MY
GUEST..

10-15

"JOE ESKIMO AND JOE JACKET WERE RIVALS
FOR THE HEART OF SALLY SNOW WHO LIVED
SOUTH OF THE ICEBERG....JOE ESKIMO THOUGHT
BACK TO THE NIGHT HE FIRST SHOOK HER HAND"

"I THINK YOU ARE
VERY NICE,' HE HAD
TOLD HER, AND THEY
SHOOK HANDS."

THEY
SHOOK
HANDS?

I THINK
YOUR LOVE
SCENE NEEDS
A LITTLE
SOMETHING..

I ALWAYS GET
SO EMBARRASSED..

SCHULZ

PEANUTS

featuring

"Good ol' Charlie Brown"

BY SCHULZ

10-22

"FEAR OF FALLING LEAVES."...
WHEN WE GET HOME, I'LL HAVE
TO LOOK THAT ONE UP...

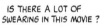

PEANUTS featuring "Good ol' Charlie Brown" by Schulz

HMM..

IT SAYS HERE THAT THE HUMMINGBIRD IS THE ONLY WINGED CREATURE THAT CAN FLAP HIS WINGS FAST ENOUGH TO BE ABLE TO HOVER MOTIONLESS IN THE AIR...

THAT'S VERY INTERESTING

11-12

KLUNK!

ONE-TENTH OF A SECOND IS NOT A HOVER!

PEANUTS
featuring
"Good ol'
CharlieBrown"
by Schulz

flitter flitter flitter flitter flitter

HI,
FEATHERS!

WOODSTOCK
JUST HATES
TO BE CALLED
"FEATHERS"

!

HEE HEE
HEE HEE
HEE!

11-19

BANANA
NOSE?!

HEE
HEE
HEE

!

I GUESS IT'S BEST
TO COME OUT EVEN...

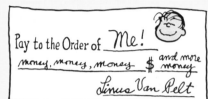

PEANUTS featuring "Good ol' Charlie Brown" by Schulz

Pay to the Order of **Me!**
money, money, money $ and more money
Linus Van Pelt

HA!! LOOK AT THAT!

IT'S STARTING TO SNOW, AND I'M **READY**!

I'M GOING TO BE THE FIRST KID IN THE NEIGHBORHOOD TO SHOVEL WALKS..

I'M GOING FROM HOUSE TO HOUSE, AND I'M GOING TO SHOVEL EVERY SIDEWALK AND DRIVEWAY THAT I CAN FIND!

WILL YOU MAKE A LOT OF MONEY?

YOU BET I'LL MAKE A LOT OF MONEY! AND YOU THINK I'LL SPEND IT RIGHT AWAY, DON'T YOU? WELL, I WON'T!

I'LL PROBABLY PUT IT ALL IN A SAVINGS ACCOUNT, AND JUST LIVE OFF THE INTEREST, OR MAYBE I'LL BUY AN ANNUITY PAYABLE AT AGE TWELVE, OR MAYBE I'LL INVEST IT ALL IN SOME MUTUAL FUNDS, OR EVEN BUY SOME STOCK IN ONE OF OUR LOCAL COMPANIES THAT SEEMS TO BE GETTING BIGGER, OR...

..OR MAYBE I'LL... I'LL...

I REMEMBER READING ABOUT ABRAHAM LINCOLN, AND HOW HE USED TO DO HIS HOMEWORK WITH A PIECE OF COAL ON THE BACK OF A SHOVEL...

FORGET IT!

11-26

PEANUTS featuring "Good ol' Charlie Brown" by SCHULZ

STAY!

GO BACK! STAY!

GO BACK!

BACK, I SAY! BACK!

1-14

✳SIGH✳ SOME KIDS HAVE DOGS WHO TRY TO FOLLOW THEM TO SCHOOL...

PEANUTS
featuring
"Good ol' CharlieBrown"
by Schulz

DO YOU WANT TO TAKE ME TO THE SENIOR PROM?

THAT WON'T BE FOR ANOTHER TEN YEARS

I JUST WANTED TO GIVE YOU A BREAK...IN TEN YEARS I PLAN TO BE THE MOST SOUGHT-AFTER GIRL IN SCHOOL!

I HAVE NO INTENTION TO SEEK AFTER YOU..

WELL, IF YOU DO, I'LL BE STANDING BY THE DRINKING FOUNTAIN AT THE NORTH END OF THE BUILDING!!

THERE'S NO SENSE TO BEING SOUGHT AFTER IF YOU CAN'T BE FOUND!

PEANUTS featuring "Good ol' Charlie Brown" by Schulz

TRUE!! FALSE?

QUESTION NUMBER ONE...

TRUE!

TRUE AGAIN! FALSE!

TRUE, BY GOLLY! AND FALSE AND TRUE AND TRUE!

FALSE AGAIN!! THERE'S NO DOUBT ABOUT IT!

™ Reg. U.S. Pat. Off. — All rights reserved
© 1973 by United Feature Syndicate, Inc.

TRUE! THAT ONE IS ABSOLUTELY TRUE!

FALSE! FALSE! FALSE! TRUE!

2-4

OH, I SAY THIS ONE IS REALLY FALSE!!

TRUE! FALSE! TRUE! FALSE! TRUE! FALSE!

TRUE, BY GOLLY! TRUE!!

PSST! PATTY!

HUH? WHAT? WHAT'S THE MATTER? HUH?

YOU WERE GETTING KIND OF LOUD..

HOW EMBARRASSING

IT'S EASY TO GET CARRIED AWAY IN THESE TRUE OR FALSE TESTS...

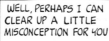

PEANUTS featuring "Good ol' Charlie Brown" by Schulz

NOW SHOWING

"Life Goes On!"

DO YOU THINK THAT THINGS CHANGE AS WE GET OLDER, CHUCK?

WELL, MY DAD HAS TOLD ME ABOUT THIS VERY NICE THEATER THAT USED TO BE IN THE NEIGHBORHOOD WHERE HE GREW UP...

WHEN HE WAS VERY SMALL, THE THEATER SEEMED HUGE, BUT AS THE YEARS WENT BY, THE THEATER GOT NARROWER AND NARROWER...

NARROWER AND NARROWER? HOW COULD A THEATER GET NARROWER AND NARROWER?

ARE YOU GETTING PHILOSOPHICAL ON ME, CHUCK?

MAYBE THERE COMES A TIME, WHEN YOU GET EVEN OLDER, WHEN THE THEATER BECOMES WIDE AGAIN...

GIRLS DON'T LIKE IT WHEN A BOY GETS PHILOSOPHICAL, CHUCK

I'M GOING HOME...I HAVE A FEELING THAT OUR BACK YARD IS SHRINKING...

2-18

PEANUTS
featuring
"Good ol' Charlie Brown"
by SCHULZ

AHEM!

IT'S NOT SIX O'CLOCK YET! I REFUSE TO FEED YOU EVEN ONE MINUTE BEFORE SIX O'CLOCK!

I KNOW YOU! I'M ON TO YOUR LITTLE GAME!

TODAY YOU WANT TO BE FED AT FIVE O'CLOCK... TOMORROW IT WOULD BE FOUR O'CLOCK.. THE NEXT DAY IT WOULD BE THREE O'CLOCK..

PRETTY SOON YOU'D HAVE WORKED YOUR WAY BACK AROUND THE CLOCK, AND YOU'D HAVE PICKED UP AN EXTRA SUPPER!

WELL, YOU CAN JUST FORGET IT!

HE'S SMARTER THAN I THOUGHT HE WAS!

2-25

SCHULZ

PEANUTS
featuring
"Good ol' Charlie Brown"
by SCHULZ

CRUNCH

YOU KNOW WHAT MAKES KIND OF A GOOD HOBBY? SAVING STRING!

PEANUTS
featuring
"Good ol' Charlie Brown"
by SCHULZ

PAT PAT PAT

WHAT IN THE WORLD ARE YOU DOING?

PAT PAT

PATTING BIRDS ON THE HEAD... I HAVE FOUND THAT WHENEVER I GET REALLY DEPRESSED, PATTING BIRDS ON THE HEAD CHEERS ME UP...

THE BIRDS ALSO SEEM TO LIKE IT

SIGH

3-11

THERE ARE OTHER WAYS TO CURE DEPRESSION...YOU DON'T HAVE TO PAT BIRDS ON THE HEAD!

SO CUT IT OUT!!

boot

PEANUTS featuring "Good ol' Charlie Brown" by SCHULZ

POW!

3-25

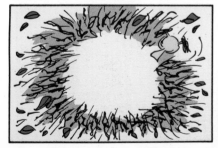

PEANUTS
featuring
"Good ol'
Charlie Brown"
by Schulz

HE'S COMING! HE'S COMING!

4-22

THANK YOU, EASTER BEAGLE! THANK YOU!

THANK YOU

THANK YOU VERY MUCH

THANK YOU

THANK YOU!

EVERYBODY GETS AN EGG FROM THE EASTER BEAGLE

WHO DO I GET ONE FROM?

HIS ASSISTANT!

PEANUTS featuring "Good ol' Charlie Brown" by Schulz

WHAAA!

!

DON'T CRY, RERUN...

WAAH!

PLEASE DON'T CRY...

WHAH

WHAT'S GOING ON?

RERUN FOUND OUT THAT HE'S STAYING HOME WHILE THE REST OF US ARE GOING OUT TO DINNER...

SO WHAT'S THE PROBLEM? HE'LL BE WITH A GOOD SITTER...

A SITTER?

THAT'S DIFFERENT... WHAT A RELIEF

4-29

I WAS AFRAID THEY WERE GOING TO PUT ME IN A KENNEL!

PEANUTS
featuring
"Good ol' Charlie Brown"
by SCHULZ

Dear Contributor,
We regret to inform you that your manuscript does not suit our present needs.
The Editors

AAAH!

BAM!

5-6

C R A S H

STOMP! STOMP!
STOMP! STOMP!

WHAM!

P.S. Don't take it out on your mailbox.

SCHULZ

PEANUTS

featuring
"Good ol' Charlie Brown"
by Schulz

MOM?

SNIF!

THAT'S THE SADDEST THING I'VE EVER SEEN.. ESPECIALLY ON MOTHER'S DAY...

OF COURSE, WHO AM I TO TALK?

5-13

I DON'T KNOW WHERE MY MOM IS EITHER... I DON'T KNOW WHERE MY DAD IS OR ANY OF MY BROTHERS OR SISTERS..

THAT'S TERRIBLE..

WHERE IS EVERYBODY?

Schulz

PEANUTS
featuring
"Good ol' Charlie Brown"
by SCHULZ

"I love you," she said, and together they laughed. Then one day she said, "I hate you," and they cried. But not together.

"What happened to the love that we said would never die?" she asked. "It died," he said.

Tm Reg. U.S. Pat. Off.—All rights reserved
© 1973 by United Feature Syndicate, Inc.

The first time he saw her she was playing tennis. The last time he saw her she was playing tennis.

5-27

"Ours was a Love set," he said, "but we double-faulted." "You always talked a better game than you played," she said.

THAT'S VERY GOOD... NOW ALL YOU NEED IS A TITLE...

A Love Story by Erich Beagle

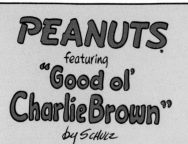

PEANUTS
featuring
"Good ol' Charlie Brown"
by Schulz

LUCY VAN PELT

FLAWLESS ADVICE

PSYCHIATRIC HELP 5¢

THE DOCTOR IS [IN]

SO FOR ALL I KNOW, I'M WRONG!

PSYCHIATRIC HELP 5¢

THE DOCTOR IS [IN]

MY TROUBLE IS I NEVER KNOW IF I'M DOING THE RIGHT THING

I NEED TO HAVE SOMEONE AROUND WHO CAN TELL ME WHEN I'M DOING THE RIGHT THING...

OKAY... YOU'RE DOING THE RIGHT THING... THAT'LL BE FIVE CENTS, PLEASE!

6-10

THE DOCTOR IS [IN]

PSYCHIATRIC HELP 5¢

THE DOCTOR IS [IN]

BACK ALREADY? WHAT HAPPENED?

THE DOCTOR IS [IN]

I WAS WRONG... IT DIDN'T HELP..

YOU NEED MORE IN LIFE THAN JUST HAVING SOMEONE AROUND TO TELL YOU WHEN YOU'RE DOING THE RIGHT THING...

NOW, YOU'VE REALLY LEARNED SOMETHING! THAT'LL BE ANOTHER FIVE CENTS, PLEASE!

THE DOCTOR IS [IN]

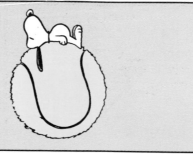

PEANUTS
featuring
"Good ol' Charlie Brown"
by Schulz

7-8

I'VE NEVER SEEN IT TO FAIL!

FIND A GOOD SPOT, AND EVERYONE ELSE MOVES IN!

PEANUTS
featuring
"Good ol' CharlieBrown"
by SCHULZ

STILL MOPING? I CAN'T BELIEVE IT!

BUT THAT WAS ALMOST TEN WEEKS AGO!

I CAN'T HELP IT!

I'LL NEVER GET OVER IT! NEVER!!

WELL, WHY DON'T YOU WRITE A LETTER OR SOMETHING LIKE YOU SAID YOU WERE GOING TO DO? MAYBE THAT WILL HELP...

7-15

I GUESS I WILL...

Dear Bobby Riggs,
You were lucky!!!

SCHULZ

PEANUTS featuring "Good ol' Charlie Brown" by SCHULZ

Their Love Was Not in the Cards

"You've always ignored me," she said. "And now you say you want to marry me."

"Every night you play cards."

"I'm really afraid," she said, "that you love cards more than you love me."

"If you could say something nice to me just once, perhaps I'd marry you."

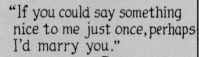

" ♦ ♣ ♥ ♠ "

"You blew it!" she said, and walked out of his life forever.

8-26

PEANUTS
featuring
"Good ol' Charlie Brown"
by SCHULZ

BLEAH!

SOMEBODY'S ALWAYS STIRRING UP THE ENEMY!

9-2

HA! YOU DIDN'T THINK I COULD GET MENTIONED, BUT I DID!

I DON'T KNOW WHAT YOU'RE TALKING ABOUT..

THE SCHOOL PLAY! THE PROGRAM WHERE EVERYONE GETS MENTIONED!

9-9

SEE? THEY HAVE THE NAMES OF ALL THE KIDS WHO WERE IN THE PLAY, AND THEY HAVE THE NAMES OF ALL THE ADULTS WHO HELPED WITH SCENERY AND FOOD AND THINGS...

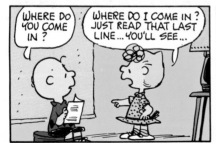

WHERE DO YOU COME IN?

WHERE DO I COME IN? JUST READ THAT LAST LINE... YOU'LL SEE...

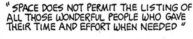

"SPACE DOES NOT PERMIT THE LISTING OF ALL THOSE WONDERFUL PEOPLE WHO GAVE THEIR TIME AND EFFORT WHEN NEEDED"

BY GOLLY, DON'T TELL ME I'M NOT IMPORTANT ENOUGH TO GET MENTIONED!

I'M COMPLETELY CONVINCED!

Other *Snoopy* books published by Ravette

Colour landscapes in this series

First Serve	£2.95
Be Prepared	£2.95
Stay Cool	£2.95
Shall We Dance?	£2.95
Come Fly With Me	£2.95
Let's Go	£2.95
Hit The Headlines	£2.95

Black and white landscapes

It's a Dog's Life	£2.50
Roundup	£2.50
Freewheelin'	£2.50
Joe Cool	£2.50
Dogs Don't Eat Dessert	£2.50
You're on the Wrong Foot Again, Charlie Brown	£2.50

Snoopy Stars series

No 1	The Flying Ace	£1.95
No 2	The Matchmaker	£1.95
No 3	The Terror Of The Ice	£1.95
No 4	The Legal Beagle	£1.95
No 5	The Head Boy	£1.95
No 6	Man's Best Friend	£1.95
No 7	The Sportsman	£1.95
No 8	The Scourge of the Fairways	£1.95
No 9	The Branch Manager	£1.95
No 10	The World Famous Literary Ace	£1.95
No 11	The Great Pretender	£1.95
No 12	The Dog-Dish Gourmet	£1.95

All these books are available at your local bookshop or newsagent, or can be ordered direct from the publisher. Just tick the titles you require and fill in the form below. Prices and availability subject to change without notice.

Ravette Books Limited, 3 Glenside Estate, Star Road, Partridge Green, Horsham, West Sussex RH13 8RA

Please send a cheque or postal order and allow the following for postage and packing. UK: 45p for one book plus 30p for each additional book.

Name ....

Address ....

....